C000258569

LUCY'S VILLAGE

LUCY'S VILLAGE

a story for a little girl by
Ada Harrison and
Robert Austin

Scolar Press
London

First published in 1945
by Oxford University Press;
This edition entirely re-set, re-originated,
and published 1979 by Scolar Press,
90/91 Great Russell Street,
London WC1B 3PS

© 1945, 1979 Robert Austin

Printed and bound in Great Britain
by W & J Mackay Limited, Chatham

ISBN 0 85967 524 6

Lucy's Village

Here is a place where I have never been;
Here are people I have never seen.
Yet I see the people and the place I know.
They belonged to my Nannie, years and
years ago.

When my Nannie was a little girl her
name was Lucy;
She lived in a cottage with a pear-tree at
the gate.
They smothered the green pears till they
were gold and juicy.
They were the sweetest things my Nannie
ever ate.

Outside the gate was an old-fashioned
        village:
A church with a steeple and ducks on the
        pond,
The green, and houses for a handful of
        people,
And only the meadows and the fields
        beyond.

It's fifty years and more since my Nannie
        had a sight of it—
It's terrible to think how time goes
        bowling by;
But the street with the cottages and shops
        to left and right of it,
She sees it all as fresh as paint, and
        so do I . . .

Mr. Boyce the butcher, and the cobbler,
      Mr. Heather,
Mr. Bolt the blacksmith, who lived at the
      forge;
The little all-sorts shop kept by Mrs.
      Merryweather,
And the bakehouse opposite the "Royal
      George."

There the men used to sit in the summer
      evenings
To bowl their bowls, and argue in a great
      loud voice.
The butcher had a wooden leg, and once
      had been a sailor.
My Nannie was afraid of Mr. Boyce.

Mr. Matchett at the bakehouse was
        always busy;
Even on a Sunday he didn't have a rest.
They took him their apple-pies to bake for
        Sunday dinner.
He was kind and he was floury . . . Lucy
        liked him best.

Everyone was busy when my Nannie was
        little.
She didn't have to idle her time away
        with toys.
Even when she was tiny she could peg out
        washing,
And help to mind her brothers, the
        mischievous boys.

She could sweep and she could dust, she
       could stir porridge and pick
       currants,
She could knit and she could iron, she
       could run and fell.
And when she and her brothers all
       worked together
They could wind the great bucket to the
       top of the well.

The well was a danger and one had to be
       afraid of it.
Old Granny had stories that made the
       flesh creep
Of children who had pushed the lid and
       scrambled up the coping,
And gone falling, falling to the water dark
       and deep.

Old Granny used to sit in the
        chimney-corner,
A little old woman with a wrinkled-apple
        face.
Day in, day out, her hands were always
        busy
Throwing the bobbins for her pillow lace.

When the boys were in bed Lucy sat at
        her knee,
And the tales her Granny told her she still
        tells to me.
From her Granny's Granny are the tales
        I'm told,
So they must be hundreds and hundreds
        of years old.

I like best to hear of how Lucy was
      naughty,
Terrible naughty one hot August day.
She was eleven and in charge of the
      children.
Her father was at harvest, and her mother
      away.

The boys came and begged her to help
      them get ripe apricots—
Not stealing, because they hung over the
      wall
Right into the lane, so they couldn't be
      anyone's.
Alone they couldn't reach them, but Lucy
      was tall.

Lucy knew well enough how stealing was
     stealing;
She told them to be off to the common or
     the brook.
But they stayed about the house and
     worried her and teased her
With, "Just come and look, Lucy. Just
     have one look."

Golden, pink-cheeked, freckled hung the
     apricots
Like fruit in a fairytale, like nothing that
     she'd seen;
The strangeness, she still remembers, was
     what made her do it . . .
In a moment she was up among the dark
     and glossy green,

And in another moment she was down.
　　She heard the branches
Crashing and cracking with the weight of
　　her fall,
The terrible voice of the gardener
　　shouting . . .
And then she remembers nothing more at
　　all.

All the time she lay in bed her father
      never spoke to her,
Nor came nigh nor by her, nor showed
      her his face.
I always cry a bit when she comes to this
      part of it . . .
The pain and the broken arm, and then
      the disgrace.

I think it was hard of him, but Lucy
    understands it.
By the end of harvest all was mended and
    healed.
She took her tea up with the boys where
    they were cutting,
And waited for the finish of the last big
    field.

Sunset and moonrise then they saw
    together;
She held her father's hand at the edge of
    the crowd,
The standing square of wheat in the
    middle growing smaller,
The cutter never far away, but whirring
    close and loud . . .

All waiting, waiting with the huge moon
          rising on them,
Every boy with a stick and every man
          with a gun,
And the rabbits pressed in and in the
          shrinking corn-patch
Waiting with their bursting hearts, ready
          to run.

Then came the bad part; she shuddered
          but she watched it.
The good part was riding home on Jill,
          close pressed
To her father, jog-jog, and the moon, and
          no one speaking.
One knew he was the kind of man who
          liked girls best.

They stumbled down at last to lamplight
        and supper
Piping-hot. She was so sleepy she could
        hardly hold her spoon.
Her mother laughed and fed her and took
        her up. The whiteness
Was like snow outside. Then at last no
        more moon.

Lovely it was: I can feel by how she tells
        it.
I have my pleasures and my treats, I
        know,
But the things they did were different
        when Lucy was little.
I wish I could have lived with them, fifty
        years ago.

Lucy laughs when I say it, and tells me
      I'm joking,
And asks how a fine lady like me would
      get along
With hard work and no toys and no big
      house and no schooling,
But in her heart I don't believe she thinks
      I'm wrong.

Sometimes I ask her what happened to
      her brothers.
Ben ran away to America, because
He was the wideawake and get-rich-quick
      sort.
Tom couldn't leave horses, so he stayed
      where he was,

And worked on the same farm, and lived
     in the next village,
And was father of a family of tumbling
     girls and boys.
My Nannie didn't see them much; his
     wife was a poor thing . . .
Never had the cottage free of clutter and
     noise.

Another thing I like to hear is how she
     had a shilling.
She was given one once for a song she'd
     sung.
She was swinging on the gate, and a lady
     passed and heard her.
A shilling was a fortune when my Nannie
     was young.

She still can't remember what she did
        with the rest of it,
But she ran to the all-sorts shop, and,
        taking no advice,
She spent three whole pennies on
        enormous brown humbugs.
I should have chosen the sugar mice.

From the time she was tiny she had
      always minded babies,
Their own, or anyone's that came her
      way.
She liked to have one handy; she supposes
      she was born to it.
At last, when she was fourteen, there
      came a day

When she put on a new lilac frock and
       starched white apron,
Said Good-bye to her Granny, and more
       timid than a mouse,
Set out with her mother, and her clothes
       in a new basket,
To begin work in earnest at the big White
       House.

Now she had to learn all the things they
       do in nurseries;
She never would have dreamed that there
       could be so much.
She didn't come within a mile of the baby
       in his cradle.
He lay like a little king, not for her to
       touch.

But a time came when the house was sick
      and in trouble,
And the baby did nothing but scream and
      cry.
And no one had a moment to pick him up
      and soothe him,
So when Lucy asked them timidly, they
      said, Yes, she might try.

After that her life was just babies and
      babies;
Boys or girls and good or bad, she loved
      them all the same.
When my mother was born she made up
      her mind to settle,
And of course she was waiting for me
      when I came.

I expect she'll be dead by the time that I
      have children.
It's a pity when I think that they'll never
      hear her tell
Of the pond and the green and the
      cottage with the pear-tree;
But I expect I'll manage very nearly as
      well.

For it's strange how I see the things—the
      village with the steeple,
The shops, and which house stands next
      to which in the row,
And which words come next to which in
      the Granny's stories
Of elves and dwarfs and cobblers . . .
      it's strange how I know.

When the mood is on her, in winter evenings,
      evenings,
She takes me in the armchair, in the
      firelight after tea.
She talks, and I follow, and she smooths
      me, and I wonder
Whether Lucy was the little girl, or
      whether it was me.